TWINKLE WIN

MAN'S BEST FRIEND and Your Star Signs

Cartoons and captions by Gray Jolliffe *Text by Peter Mayle*

Pan Books
London and Sydney

AMAZING ASTROLOGICAL BREAKTHROUGH

Until very recently, students and scholars have only acknowledged the influence of the stars in two areas:

But there's more to a man than his head and his heart. By applying the intellectual process known as downward lateral thinking, we can begin to see a more complete picture. There are not just two areas of astrological influence.

There are three:

How this has escaped the keenest scientific brains over the years we shall never know. Maybe these wise men were always looking upwards. Maybe their telescopes interfered with close-range vision. Who can tell? It all seems so blindingly obvious now. Indeed, the course of history is littered with clues which provide clear links between the heavens above and the rascal below, and at least one of the Seven Wonders of the World owes its very existence to Willie's inspiration.

THE TRUTH ABOUT THE PYRAMIDS

OR

THE REASON FOR THE SPHINX'S INSCRUTABLE SMILE

The ancient Egyptians, who were several thousand years ahead of Hollywood in living according to the star system, wouldn't even cross the Nile without consulting their local astrologer. In fact, the theory that has been handed down through history is that the mighty Pyramids were built not only as retirement homes for old Pharaohs, but to reflect the disposition of stars in the sky.

As is so often the case, history has omitted one or two vital details. The full story, which is illustrated by a series of little-known tomb paintings, is as follows.

It came to pass that the elderly Pharaoh was lingering on his death bed, surrounded by his trusty advisers. In hushed voices, they were discussing what form his memorial should take. (Something tasteful in marble and gold leaf? A nice obelisk, maybe?) Back and forth the discussion went.

Suddenly, the Pharaoh's personal nurse arrived with his medicine. As she bent over to administer it, a remarkable thing happened: *The Pharaoh's top sheet assumed the shape of a Pyramid*.

Lo and behold! said the advisers, a portent! Obviously, this is the form the memorial should take. It reaches for the stars, and is of pleasing proportions. Let's settle for that.

Thus it was written, and thus the Pyramids were built.

As we all know now, with the benefit of hindsight, that was no mystical portent under the Pharaoh's top sheet. It was our old friend the Scourge of Suez, responding to an attractive nurse in his normal enthusiastic fashion. Still, if history likes to think he was reaching for the stars, it makes a pleasant change from all those other stories about him.

"FUNNY, HE DOESN'T *LOOK* LIKE A CAPRICORN"

Despite that little misunderstanding over the Pyramids, there can be no reasonable doubt that Wicked Willie's behaviour *is* affected by astrological influences. Now for the first time, we shall reveal the cosmic forces that shape his personality and lifestyle, the supernatural stimuli that provoke his unpredictable moods, his bursts of energy, his smiles, his frowns, his ups, his downs.

Yes, it's the world's first astrogenital zodiac.

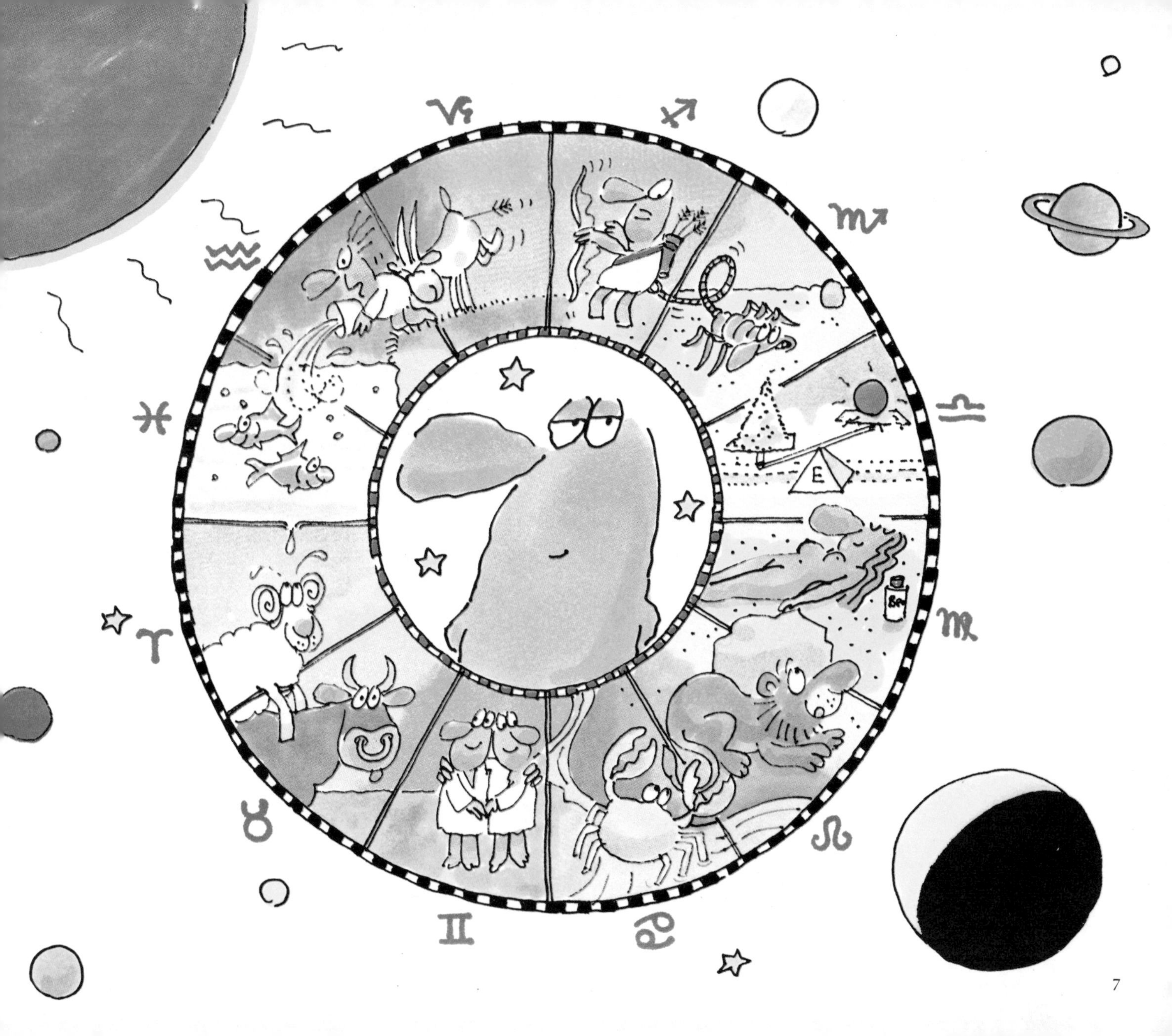

AQUARIUS

The Water Bearer
21st January – 19th February

Many scholars and scientists, and a good proportion of the membership of the Book of the Month Club, are Aquarians.

They are intelligent and rational, original, inventive, self-assured and tolerant. They are almost unbearable. Fortunately, they have a fatal flaw: they can't resist joining things. They join causes. They join clubs. They join movements and organizations. If an Aquarian sees three people outside a phone booth, he'll apply for membership. Have you ever wondered who supports the Society for the Protection of Hedgehogs, or the Concerned Citizens Against Polyester, or the SDP? Aquarians.

This is all to the good as far as Willie is concerned. He is happy to pose as a concerned, intelligent and rational Aquarian, because he too loves to join in. Any active movement involving two people will suit him very well.

MEDIA REVIEW
PULL OUT SECTION ON: POLAND
Who'd believe we have the same birth sign?

Ideal Woman

She must be witty and stimulating, with a well-developed social conscience and membership of at least one organization. Or she must have a well-developed intellect. Or maybe it's enough just to be well-developed. Aquarians are only human.

Do you like Dickens?
COLLEGE LIBRARY BAR
Yeah - but not on a first date!

PISCES

The Fishes
20th February – 20th March

A varied and surprising bunch, Pisceans. Where else in the Zodiac do you find poets and actors, doctors and nurses, masochists and alcoholics all sharing the same sign?

The trouble is that the Piscean, a kind, sensitive and idealistic soul, often finds the world a distressing place, and will look for a means of escape. This may take the form of a double gin or a bad sonnet or an unhealthy obsession with amateur theatricals, and it is usually accompanied by a guilt complex.

For a simple, fun-loving soul like our Willie, to be attached to a Piscean can be most baffling. On the one hand you have guilt and masochism, which do not feature in his plans for a good time. On the other hand, you have escapism and nurses, which definitely do. That is the eternal conflict, and that is why many Pisceans suffer from moods of depression and delusions of poetry.

Dont look at me.
He's the wino!
Z
Z
Z
Z
Z
Z

Ideal Woman

Someone with a good bedside manner, a thorough knowledge of practical psychiatry, and her own off-licence.

It's not your fault – I often get post orgasmic depression.
Post fake-orgasmic depression, actually.

ARIES

The Ram
21st March – 20th April

Spring begins officially when the sun enters the sign of Aries, and we all know what that means: the sap starts to rise and a young man's fancy lightly turns away from football.

It will come as no surprise, therefore, to find that Willie the Ram (as he fondly imagines himself) is quick, energetic and active. He is also impulsive, and will dive head first into situations which a more cautious temperament would avoid altogether. And as if that weren't bad enough, he is subconsciously attracted to uniforms and danger.

A disastrous mixture. When you combine a love of risk with a high level of activity, trouble is never far away. Indeed, Arian Willie seems to thrive on it, because there is a strong streak of vanity in his nature. He likes to think he performs well under pressure, and he'll jump at the chance to show off.

Don't worry - just hand over the froggy outfit and leave the talking to me.

Ideal Woman

Picture if you can a woman in uniform with violent tendencies and an honours degree in the martial arts, and there you have an irresistible challenge. To Willie, the thought of a partner who might at any time launch a flying kick at his hopes and dreams is intensely stimulating, and will keep him, so to speak, on his toes.

OW!
OUCH!!
I have to keep pinching
nyself to make sure I'm
not dreaming..

TAURUS

The Bull
21st April – 21st May

Taurean Willie is a character you can lean on. He is reliable and patient, and famous in astrological circles for his determined persistence in the face of obstacles. (Depending on the circumstances, this determination can lead to tearful gratitude or a smack in the face; you never know until you try.)

But just as every silver lining has its cloud, so Willie's virtues have their drawbacks. If you catch them on a bad day, they can appear to be obstinacy and resistance to change, and a boring refusal to try anything new. The only way round this is to tempt him by appealing to the side of the Taurean character that responds to beauty, luxury and good food, preferably all at once.

A warning: the Taurean is jealous and possessive. If upset, he will sulk. If ignored, he will get his own back by letting you down next time you want him to be patient and reliable.

COMPANY
What Holiday
Which What
What Car?
What Beer
WHAT MICRO
WHAT PUSSY
Campaign

Ideal Woman

One side of Willie's Taurean character needs obstacles, so that he can demonstrate his persistence. The other side has a passion for luxury and good food. Put them together, and the ideal woman is one who sits up in bed between satin sheets defending her honour by throwing pots of caviar and platefuls of lobster Thermidor every time Willie pokes his head round the door.

Why do you have a mirror on your dining room ceiling?
Because the shmuck prefers eating to sex.

GEMINI

The Twins
22nd May – 21st June

Admirers of the Gemini character describe it as quick-thinking and adaptable, spurred on by a restless curiosity. Most Geminis will agree with this. But it's only fair to say that the sign has its critics, and according to them, the typical Gemini is fickle, shallow, two-faced and not to be trusted at parties.

Everything is true. Gemini Willie is such a contradictory creature he often doesn't know himself whether he's coming or going. All he knows for sure is that he thrives on variety, and this often means that he has to perform miracles of juggling in order to keep all his balls in the air at the same time. It sounds uncomfortable, but to Willie anything is better than being bored.

I just wish he'd learn to be good at one thing instead of average at a lot.

Ideal Woman

Bearing in mind the craving for variety, the logical choice here would be a harem. However, the law of the land and prohibitive housing costs being what they are, the answer is probably one ingenious woman with a talent for disguise and a wardrobe full of wigs.

propose we go doors and fool around.
I propose we don't.
VAGUE
All those 'against'!
All those 'For'
That's cheating!

CANCER

The Crab
22nd June – 22nd July

Until you know what governs it, the Cancerian character can be something of a mystery. Kind and sympathetic one day, irritable and hypersensitive the next, it may seem to be totally unpredictable. In fact, it begins to make sense when you realize that lunar influences are hard at work here. Cancerian Willie is ruled by the moon. Hence his waxing and waning, his romantic streak, his tendency to get a bit out of hand during periods of full moon, his depression and desire for solitude at other times of the month. Get yourself one of those charts that show the lunar phases and you'll be able to read him like a book.

Apart from its links with the moon, Cancer is also the maternal sign of the Zodiac, a fact which causes Willie a certain amount of worry and confusion, and which in extreme cases can lead to an identity crisis.

Or Madam may prefer one of our less discreet gifts?

Ideal Woman

A fortune teller, a weather forecaster – any woman with sufficient knowledge of the moon to be compatible. (i.e. She won't want to wax while you're on the wane, and vice versa.)

Of course, I only read it for the articles...
What a whopper!
thanks!
PLAYBOY

LEO

The Lion
23rd July – 23rd August

The Leo character is forceful, confident and fancies himself as the King of Beasts. Willie the Leo is equally sure of himself, instinctively feeling that his place in the world is on top (the Missionary complex), and that others should defer to his will.

It is this self-confidence allied to a highly-developed organizational ability that makes Leos very good at being Managing Directors of public companies or high-ranking officers in the armed forces. They make excellent dictators, too.

In fairness, all is not naked ambition and lust for domination in the Leo character. He is warm-hearted. He has many friends. He is not afraid of tackling anything, no matter how big. He is extravagant (always an endearing characteristic). He is dignified and courageous. In a sentence, he believes himself to be great, and believes that greatness should be thrust upon him.

Aw c'mon - just a quickie - then get up.

Ideal Woman

When you want to have greatness thrust upon you, there is no more agreeable sight than that of a generously proportioned woman. If, in addition, she has a liking for discipline, this will take care of the military/organizational side of your requirements. And if she likes to dress up as a Brigadier in the W.R.A.C., so much the better. You can then pull rank.

So she was too fat. Big deal – what are you, Mr. goddam Universe?

VIRGO

The Virgin
24th August – 23rd September

Right away we have a problem with the name. Lions and rams and bulls and even crabs are all very well, but *virgins*? How can Willie the Virgin hold his head up?

Well, he compensates. He is the hardest worker in the Zodiac, and you can take that how you will. He is obsessed with detail, and he likes to give good service. He has a great deal of nervous energy and a keen intellect. In other words, he's the kind of star sign you can introduce to your mother or your bank manager.

But – and it's something you should know before it's too late – he has a longing for purity, hygiene, wholesome diets and clean living that is not altogether healthy. You can imagine him eloping with a nutritionist and a month's supply of muesli.

If that particular urge can be kept under control, Virgo Willie is as good as the next sign, and a lot better intellectually. Not for nothing is he known as the egghead of the zodiac.

STEP BY STEP DIRTY BOOK
Just my luck to get stuck with a sexual Sunday driver.

Ideal Woman

A qualified physicist with several sets of clean leotards and a fondness for anything free range or organically grown. Jacuzzi preferred but not essential. (You can always make do with a bath and half a dozen Alka-Seltzer tablets.)

I've always thought of you as one of the boys, Elaine.
He's getting his new contact lenses next week.

LIBRA

The Scales
24th September – 23rd October

As you would expect from the sign, the Libran character is balanced and harmonious, reasonable and fair. Librans are often good politicians or diplomats. From time to time, though, we see some very naughty politicians and diplomats, caught in compromising situations with their defences down and their trousers nowhere to be seen. Newspaper reports may blame these lapses on pressure of work, but we know better. There is a streak in the Libran character that is frivolous and self-indulgent. And where do we find that streak? You guessed it.

Libran Willie is a sucker for a good time. He hates to be on his own, loves to be entertained, and will flirt with almost anything. (Libran politicians, as is well known, will even kiss babies if there's nobody else available.) Only laziness and lack of cash will prevent him from being a full-time playboy, and you can never count on his good behaviour for long. In political terms, a vote from him is a vote for trouble.

I thought doctors weren't supposed to advertise.

Ideal Woman

Any woman who thinks he's wonderful has a head start with Libran Willie. It means they have something in common. He is also attracted to the female floating voter.

Tell her to forget it.
I have my pride!

SCORPIO

The Scorpion
24th October – 22nd November

Many astrologers will tell you that this is the most passionate sign in the Zodiac, and you won't get any arguments from Willie the Scorpion.

His feelings are intense. He needs to dominate. He will use his personal magnetism to have his way with you, and the force of his character makes him a natural leader.

These characteristics, while undoubtedly useful in a lion tamer or the headmaster of a school for wayward girls, are not without their darker side. There are several stings in the Scorpion's tail. He can be jealous, violent, sarcastic and suspicious. Willie, of course, would deny this, much preferring to promote the personal magnetism angle and keep the rest of it quiet. But in fact, there is a secretive side to the Scorpio nature which can cause some nasty surprises. You never know when the urge to dominate and be magnetic will show itself, and this makes cocktail parties and games of mixed doubles socially risky.

Phone nos.
I said 'before you make that call, better take a look at this.

Ideal Woman

Gentle, retiring creatures don't have much of a chance. The perfect mate for a Scorpion can stand up for herself in an argument and throw a good right hand punch. This will keep him from getting big-headed.

YOU ARE HERE
Sometimes you both need putting in your place.

SAGITTARIUS

The Archer
23rd November – 21st December

An item of highly confidential information supplied by a friend in the police tells us that more convicted flashers are born under Sagittarius than under any other sign. Coincidence? Not at all. It's one more example of astrological forces ruling our lives, our destinies and our choice of outdoor recreation.

Sagittarians are extroverts. They are confident, impulsive, enthusiastic and optimistic. They enjoy being in the limelight and showing the world what they can do. They love travel and adventure. In other words, the Sagittarian character provides support and encouragement for Willie's worst and most irresponsible instincts. He needs little enough excuse to behave badly at the best of times, but when it can be blamed on the stars there's no holding him.

Your only consolation is that Sagittarian Willie becomes bored if nobody takes any notice of him; with luck, this might prompt him to sulk in a dark corner and leave you in peace.

so much for hang gliding.

Ideal Woman

Given his love of travel and hatred of being tied down, the woman of Willie's dreams is obviously an airline stewardess who won't make him fasten his seat belt.

Its kind of you, old bean, but I hate to see you spending your valuable time and hard-earned money on something I really dont want!

CAPRICORN

The Goat
22nd December – 20th January

Life to the Capricorn is a serious business. He is cautious and hard-working, patient and practical. He dislikes change, and is often pessimistic. Above all, he is ambitious, and always concerned about his position in the world.

Willie is concerned about his position, too, but he's up against almost impossible odds. He can cope with the Capricorn desire to reach the top.

The Capricorn dislike of a subordinate position is limiting, but nothing to get too worried about. It's when you add the third characteristic – the Capricorn's insistence on keeping both feet on the ground – that even Willie at his most optimistic experiences grave doubts about the fairness of life. There are limits to what can be achieved with both feet on the ground.

Tonight we're going out with someone special, so I want you to be on your best behaviour.

A romantic dinner, a quiet conversation, find out all about her interests, her likes, dislikes...

Just remember – it's a first date so sex is out of the question!

Whaddya mean, in that case you're not going??

Ideal Woman

An acrobat.

I won't be at work today, Mr Pibworth. I've been awake all night with something terrible I picked up yesterday...

HEY THERE – YOU WITH THE STARS IN YOUR EYES, THROAT, LIVER, HIPS AND LUMBAR REGION

Long, long ago, in the days when Hippocrates was a fashionable neighbourhood doctor, a young student came to him with an interesting theory. If the stars could exert such great influence on our characters, could it be that they also exert a similar influence on the various parts of our bodies?

'My God!', said Hippocrates (it was the first recorded uttering of the Hippocratic Oath), 'I think you've got something there. Off you go and do a thesis.'

The rest is history. It is now accepted that different signs of the Zodiac do rule different parts of the body. Aries rules the head. Sagittarius rules the liver, hips and thighs. Leo rules the heart and back, and so on.

The truth of this theory can easily be demonstrated by taking all the most disreputable attributes of the entire planetary system and finding their focal point. What part of the anatomy springs to mind from the following description: selfish, single-minded, unreliable, determined, boastful, shameless, devious and unfaithful?

What else?

The future is at it's best when it's less than ten seconds away..

A VISIT TO THE FORTUNE TELLER

Now that we have examined the formative influences that shape our lives and Willie's behaviour, we must ask ourselves the cosmic question: is it possible to peep through the keyhole of time and see what lies in store? Is the hand of Fate even now about to shape Willie's destiny? Or is it chance? And when people say 'it's in the lap of the gods', what exactly are they referring to?

There's only one way to find out, and that is to consult a qualified specialist.

The interesting thing about fortune tellers is that while they all offer the same end product (the future), their ways of revealing it to you vary enormously. Fortunately, some of the more disgusting old methods involving eyes of newts and toes of frogs have become obsolete. But the bad news is that it is almost impossible nowadays to find anyone offering a sacrificial virgin service. Progress is never without its penalties.

The selection of people who claim some powers of prediction is divided quite clearly into two. First, you have the unreliable fringe operators – the charlatans who give the future a bad name. They work with tea-leaves, chicken entrails, the London Stock Exchange, or the Meteorological Office. Don't have anything to do with them. You will be better off with a fortune teller who is properly equipped with one or more of the following accessories.

To the sacrificial altar!
VIRGIN CATCHER

Sire, art thou blind?

To the Royal bedchamber!
whew!
VIRGIN CATCHER

Crystal Balls

It's important to make sure that you get the highest possible picture quality here, or you could be in trouble. There have been one or two cases recently where what looked like a tall dark stranger turned out to be an irate husband. If the picture is at all fuzzy, insist on a new ball.

A Load of Old Tarot

Apart from an involuntary spasm of interest when a game of Find the Lady or strip poker is suggested, Willie does not respond to cards. They bore him, and this makes the task of the fortune teller hopelessly difficult. You can't predict the future when your subject is fast asleep.

Cross My Palm

This method is by far the most likely to end in a satisfactory result because it is the most intimate. Personal contact is established. Psychic vibrations can pass directly between two people without any interference from the crystal ball or the knave of hearts. The fascinating contours of the hand can be explored, and when someone is admiring your Mount of Venus the immediate future looks rosy indeed.

SPACE-AGE ASTROLOGY: DOES IT HAVE A FUTURE?

The world is full of sceptics, and most of them have attacked the science of astrology at one time or another. The latest barrage of scorn comes from the generation brought up to worship computers. They believe that the silicon chip can answer any question you throw at it. Let this story be a lesson to them.

A very large and well-endowed computer was recently supplied with every conceivable scrap of information about Wicked Willie – his history, personal habits, vital statistics, past convictions, favourite colour, etc. – and asked to predict the future.

In view of his troublesome past, could Willie look forward to another few thousand years of fun and mischief? Or would common sense prevail and restrict his activities to something relatively harmless like starring in a video game? These were the momentous questions that had to be answered.

The computer whirred and chattered. The Programmers stood by, hardly daring to breathe. This, after all, was a piece of research that could change history.

At last, the computer began to answer. Without thinking, a pretty young Programmer rushed up to it and started, as she innocently thought, to help the flow of information. It proved to be too much. With a warm female hand on his printout, the computer had a spectacular malfunction all over the floor, and a priceless body of knowledge was lost forever.

All that remained was a charred strip of paper on which you can just make out the words: *There is nothing like a dame.*

Would you
please repeat that
question.........

First published 1985 by Pan Books Ltd,
Cavaye Place, London SW10 9PG

ISBN 0 330 29110 6
Printed in Great Britain by
Chorley & Pickersgill Ltd, Leeds